Introduction to Space

Introduction

to

S P A C E

By LEE A. DuBRIDGE

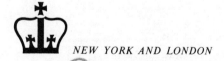

NEW YORK AND LONDON

COLUMBIA UNIVERSITY PRESS

The George B. Pegram Lectures

MUCH is said about the impact of science on society, but busy men are given few formal opportunities to make reflective appraisals of the trend of events and to communicate these appraisals in nontechnical terms. To fill this gap the George B. Pegram Lectureship was established by the Trustees of Associated Universities, Inc., to be awarded annually to an individual who has made outstanding contributions to modern society in order to provide him with a forum to discuss some area of his experience and interests dealing with the broad implications of science in our times. Residence at Brookhaven National Laboratory gives the lecturer opportunities for formal and informal contacts with the staff, and provides a period of freedom from other duties.

The study of outer space, with its implications of high adventure in peaceful exploration and dire portents in military exploitation, is a fitting subject for the first series of lectures, presented in this volume; and Dr. Lee A. DuBridge, who as research scientist, as Director of the Radiation Laboratory of the Massachusetts Institute of Technology during World War II, and in his present position as President of the California Institute of Technology has provided distinguished leadership in peace and war, is a fitting first lecturer.

The lectureship was named to honor George Braxton Pegram, one of the most influential scientists of the nuclear age. He was Professor of Physics, Dean, and Vice President of Columbia University. He was instrumental in seeing that the government was aware of the potentialities of nuclear energy in the defense of the country. In 1946 he headed the Initiatory University Group which proposed that a regional center for research in the nuclear sciences be established in the New York area and thus played a key role in the establishment of Associated Universities, Inc., and the founding of Brookhaven National Laboratory. He received many awards and honorary degrees, the last of which was the Karl Taylor Compton gold medal for distinguished service in physics, George B. Pegram's lucid mind and gentle ways will be long remembered by those who knew him. This series in his honor has been established to further his conviction that the results of science can be made to serve the needs and hopes of mankind.

R. CHRISTIAN ANDERSON
KENNETH T. BAINBRIDGE
SAMUEL A. GOUDSMIT
LELAND J. HAWORTH
DANIEL E. KOSHLAND, JR.
FRANKLIN A. LONG

Preface

IN THESE FOUR LECTURES inaugurating the George B. Pegram Lecture Series I have attempted to set forth in simple and understandable form some of the achievements of space science and technology, some of the hopes for future research in these fields, and some of the areas of great scientific interest which we will find as we come to examine our solar system more closely and as we get a better view of the more distant parts of the universe. Since these talks were intended for laymen and students, I make no apology for the fact that they are in simplified language and are possibly oversimplified. What I wished to convey is something of the difficulty as well as the excitement of space research, and some of the awesome majesty in our present concepts of the universe.

Needless to say, the material covered in these lectures was drawn from many, many sources and it would not be possible to give credit to all of them. I have had discussions with many colleagues at the California Institute of Technology and the Jet Propulsion Laboratory. Also, the following books and articles were found useful and are recommended for those who wish to pursue the subject matter further: Robert W. Buchheim and the Staff of The Rand Corporation, *Space Handbook: Astronautics and Its Applications* (New York, Random House, 1959); E. M. Burbidge, G. R. Burbidge, W. A. Fowler, and F. Hoyle, "Synthesis of the Elements in Stars," *Reviews of Modern Physics*, XXIX (October 1957), 547–650; Fred Hoyle, *Frontiers of Astronomy* (New York, Harper, 1955); *Scientific American*, 195 (September 1956), Special issue on "The Universe."

The information in the field of astronomy may be found in any elementary textbook on astronomy, such as, for example: Robert H. Baker, *Astronomy*, 7th. ed. (Princeton, D. Van Nostrand, 1959).

I am indebted to Dr. W. H. Pickering, Director of the Jet Propulsion Laboratory, and his staff for providing information about and pictures of space satellites and rockets, and to the Mount Wilson and Palomar Observatories for the astronomical photographs.

I am also indebted to the Brookhaven National Laboratory for the opportunity of delivering the first of the George B. Pegram lectures, for the cooperation of the staff of the Laboratory in making suitable arrangements for the lectures, and for publishing them.

LEE A. DUBRIDGE

Pasadena, California
January, 1960

Contents

Figures

Introduction to Space

1
Attaining a Space Orbit

THE SPACE AGE, it is said, dawned on October 4, 1957, when the Russian Sputnik I went into a free orbit around the earth, and the new age reached a fresh climax on September 13, 1959, when the Russians hit the moon.

However, astronomers have been probing the secrets of outer space for centuries. Indeed, since Galileo first turned his telescope to the heavenly bodies, astronomers have probed so far into spatial depths that the 200 or so miles above the earth attained by Sputnik, or even the 240,000 miles to the moon, would appear to be such a tiny step outward as to be utterly negligible and hardly worth all the excitement.

To illustrate: If Sputnik could have been released suddenly from the earth's gravitational pull to continue on into space with its (by earthly standards) colossal speed of 5 miles per second, it would have taken two months to reach the nearest planet (Venus), twenty-two years to reach the outermost planet (Pluto), and 150,000 years to reach the nearest star (a small star near Alpha Centauri). And that is about where astronomy is just beginning.

Clearly, not much of the astronomer's realm is to be invaded by manmade objects.

Yet, strangely enough, the astronomers have welcomed the new space age too. Not because they want to climb aboard a vehicle and journey to Alpha Centauri—or even to Pluto. The astronomer's excitement is occasioned solely by the fact that a space vehicle can now take his instruments above that murky, wiggly stuff called the earth's atmosphere which has been a major obstacle to good astronomical observations since the beginning of time. An astronomical observatory outside the atmosphere will be an astronomer's dream. And though some formidable obstacles still lie in the way, astronomers can now discuss the attainment of the dream in sober terms at august scientific meetings without being interrupted by raucous laughter.

Other pipe dreams can be soberly discussed now too. The Russians have hit the moon with a package containing a Soviet flag. Soon we can send a camera to the moon that will survive the landing. We are already planning to send a seismograph to the moon to study moonquakes. We want to find more about what the other side of the moon is like. In fact, as an oceanographer recently remarked, ruefully and somewhat vulgarly, "It is a pity that more people are interested in the moon's behind than in the ocean's bottom."

The planets too are nearly within reach and, if the huge sums of money required can be made available, some pretty spectacular ventures around the nearby portions of our solar system may soon be undertaken. Man has taken only a feeble step into the vastness of space. But he has learned how to break the gravitational chains that have always bound him to his little planet, the earth. Like a bird escaped from a cage, he may not go very far; but he is *free,* and the adventures ahead of him are such as to numb his imagination. It will be instructive and possibly even amusing to contemplate these adventures for a while.

Therefore, I am going to take an imaginary journey into space in order to see what we might see. First, I shall talk about the technological problems of getting sizable objects off the earth and free, or nearly free, of the earth's gravitational pull. Second, I shall look at some scientific problems which can be examined with the aid of such space vehicles. Third, we shall adventure into the solar system and examine the moon and the planets—their nature and possible origin, and what we may expect to find on them. Finally, we shall look at the stars, the galaxies, and the clusters of galaxies that make up our universe. We shall ask how our universe got into its present condition and where it may be going from here. In other words, we will in turn go from engineering to physics to astronomy to cosmology.

It is inaccurate to describe the attainment of space vehicles as an achievement of science; it was an achievement of engineering. The science of artificial satellites orbiting around the earth was all worked out by Newton three hundred years ago. He knew that an object projected parallel to the earth's surface at a speed of about 5 miles per second would go into a permanent orbit around the earth—if air friction were absent. It was the task of the engineer to find out how to get an object above the air and to get it moving with a speed of 5 miles per second. In principle, a rocket to achieve this end could also have been built many, many years ago. In practice, however, it was a tough engineering job. And, in fact, no useful satellites could have been launched without the development of the modern science and technology of electronics to provide the necessary guidance, control, and communications.

It is rather remarkable that, although the rocket as a holiday fireworks display had been known for a long time, the idea of using a controllable rocket as a propulsion device seems to have attracted very little attention until the experiments of Robert H. Goddard of Clark University before World War I. But Goddard was regarded as a visionary—which he was—or even as a crackpot—which he was not. And little progress on rocket technology was achieved until World War II. The story of the development of small rockets as artillery pieces by the British and Americans and of the large liquid rockets by the Germans is too well known to require repetition. Since 1946 rocket technology has proceeded along many lines and at an astonishing pace.

The story of rockets at Caltech began in 1936, when

the famed aerodynamics engineer, Professor Theodore von Kármán, became interested in the possibilities of jet and rocket propulsion. As the director of the Guggenheim Aeronautical Laboratory of the California Institute of Technology—known for short as GALCIT— he initiated a program of research and development in this field. In 1936 this was clearly a pioneering enterprise. The first practical project was to develop a rocket suitable for assisting aircraft in short take-offs. In August 1941 successful trials of a jet-assisted take-off unit —JATO—were carried out, a new company was created to manufacture such units, and a new laboratory, the Jet Propulsion Laboratory—JPL—was organized to undertake other rocket and jet propulsion research projects. In 1944 JPL was asked by the Army Ordnance Department to undertake a contract for research on large guided rockets for Army field use which would have ranges of upwards of 50 miles. A whole series of experimental rockets resulted from this effort. A notable milestone in this program occurred in 1949 when a rocket called the Bumper WAC attained an altitude of 250 miles—a record which was not exceeded thereafter for over seven years. The Bumper WAC consisted of a captured German V-2 as the booster stage and a JPL-developed WAC Corporal as the second stage. (See Fig. 1.)

After 1946 the group of German rocket engineers under Dr. Wernher von Braun initiated work at the Army's Redstone Arsenal on large liquid-propelled rockets which would be successors to the V-2. The 200-mile Redstone, and later the 1,500-mile Jupiter, came out of this effort.

In 1954 the Army asked JPL to collaborate with Redstone in the production of a rocket system which could go to extremely high altitudes in order to test the re-entry into the atmosphere of the nose cone of the Jupiter missile and other intermediate range ballistics missiles (IRBM's) and intercontinental ballistics missiles (ICBM's). Together these groups designed what was called the Jupiter-Composite, or Jupiter-C. It consisted of a Redstone booster made by the Army and three upper stages designed by JPL. These consisted of a cluster of fifteen solid-propelled rockets comprising a second stage ring of eleven rockets, a third stage of three, and a fourth stage of a single unit. To assist in guidance problems this entire cluster of fifteen rockets, plus the payload, was spin-stabilized, attaining a rotational speed of 750 r.p.m. before separation from the booster stage. (See Fig. 2.)

The first complete Jupiter-C was fired successfully in September 1956, attaining a height of 650 miles—breaking the record set in 1949 by the Bumper WAC. It also attained a record horizontal range of 3,700 miles. Two other Jupiter-C's were successfully fired, the third (in August 1957) resulting in the recovery of the nose cone exactly in the target area 1,500 miles down range. This experiment proved so adequately the success of the ablation-type nose cone that no other Jupiter-C firings

Fig. 1. Launching of the Bumper WAC rocket, 1949.

Jet Propulsion Laboratory

were deemed necessary. The several remaining units already being built were kept on the shelf.

In October 1957, after Sputnik was launched, JPL and the Army Ballistic Missile Agency (ABMA, as the Redstone group was now called) were authorized to launch a satellite using this Jupiter-C equipment. ABMA was to provide the booster stage and JPL the upper stages and the payload. Eighty days after authorization the rocket was ready to fire, but extremely bad weather at Cape Canaveral delayed the firing two days until January 31, 1958, on which date Explorer I went into orbit. (Fig. 3.) Explorers III and IV went into orbit later in 1958.

By 1959 the new Jupiter rocket was ready to replace the Redstone which had been used as a booster in the Jupiter-C's, and, using substantially improved JPL upper stages, the rocket system called "Juno" was able to fire a payload to the vicinity of the moon. (Fig. 4.) Pioneer III, launched on December 6, 1958, rose to an altitude of 63,580 miles and then returned to earth, reporting radiation data all the way out and back. Pioneer IV, launched March 3, 1959, attained more than the escape speed and sent a 13.5-pound payload past the moon and into an orbit around the sun. (Fig. 5.) Its radio signals were heard out to a distance of over 400,000 miles, at which time, after 82 hours, the batteries wore out. In the meantime, other satellites had been launched, and successes as well as failures had been experienced. (See Table I.)

Clearly, the engineers have licked the problem of us-

Fig. 2. The Jupiter-C rocket used to launch the Explorer I satellite.

Jet Propulsion Laboratory

Table I. SUMMARY OF SPACE VEHICLES SUCCESSFULLY
LAUNCHED UP TO OCTOBER 1, 1959[a]

Name	Launched	Scientific Payload (lbs.)	Perigee- Apogee (miles)	Lifetime
Sputnik I	10/4/57	184	142–588	3 months*
Sputnik II	11/3/57	1,120	140–1,038	5 months*
Explorer I	1/31/58	18.13	224–1,573	3–5 years
Vanguard I	3/17/58	3.25	409–2,453	c. 1,000 years
Explorer III	3/26/58	18.56	121–1,746	3 months*
Sputnik III	5/15/58	2,925	135–1,167	15 months*
Explorer IV	7/26/58	25.8	163–1,380	1 year*
Pioneer I	10/11/58	39	70,700 (alt.)	43.3 hours
Pioneer III	12/6/58	12.95	63,580 (alt.)	38.1 hours
Project Score	12/18/58	150	110–920	1 month*
Lunik I	1/2/59	796	solar orbit	infinite
Vanguard II	2/17/59	20.74	347–2,064	10 years
Discoverer I	2/28/59	245	99–605	6 days*
Pioneer IV	3/3/59	13.4	solar orbit	infinite
Discoverer II	4/13/59	440	142–220	13 days*
Explorer VI	8/7/59	142	156–26,357	more than 1 year
Discoverer V	8/13/59	300	136–450	1 month*
Discoverer VI	8/19/59	300	139–537	1 month*
Lunik II	9/13/59	858.4	lunar impact 236,375 miles	35 hours approx.

* No longer in orbit.

[a] Official list issued by the National Aeronautics and Space Administration.

ing guided rockets to launch sizable objects which will
1) go into earth-satellite orbits, 2) escape the earth's pull
and become other planets (or asteroids) orbiting about
the sun, or 3) land on other cosmic objects.

The rocketry required to achieve these ends is impres-
sive indeed. It is an awe-inspiring sight to see a giant
Jupiter rocket 10 feet in diameter and 76 feet high belch-
ing flame and smoke at such a rate as to produce an up-
ward thrust of 100,000 pounds or more, causing this

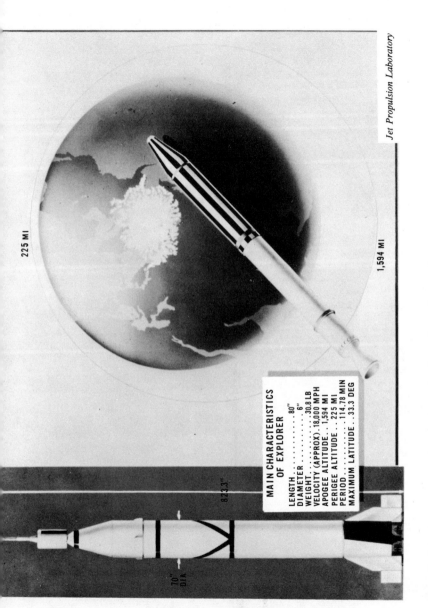

225 MI

1,594 MI

70" DIA

823.3"

**MAIN CHARACTERISTICS
OF EXPLORER**

LENGTH. . . . . 80"
DIAMETER. . . . . 6"
WEIGHT. . . . . 30.8 LB
VELOCITY (APPROX). 18,000 MPH
APOGEE ALTITUDE . . 1,594 MI
PERIGEE ALTITUDE . . . 225 MI
PERIOD. . . . . . . 114.78 MIN
MAXIMUM LATITUDE . .33.3 DEG

Jet Propulsion Laboratory

Fig. 3. The Jupiter-C rocket and the Explorer I earth sattelite.

Jet Propulsion Laboratory

Fig. 5. The Pioneer IV payload package.

huge object to rise majestically, going faster and faster, soon fading from sight as it rises and then sloughs off its huge burned-out first stage, then the second, and possibly a third. Now the relatively tiny final payload is given an enormous acceleration by the final rocket which impels it up to its orbital speed. (Fig. 6.) Yet this huge 100,000-pound Jupiter is a small booster indeed compared with a 6-million-pound-thrust monster (known as Nova) now being discussed.

But, though the rockets are big, an even more miraculous collection of electronic equipment is required for monitoring and controlling every item in the preparation of the missile for firing, in the activation of its guidance and control system, and in the operation of the payload instruments. As the huge rocket takes off, electronically controlled vanes in the jet blast keep the rocket in a vertical position. Later, other circuits program a proper turn in the direction of the final orbit, and continuously guide and control the successive stages until the firing of the last stage injects the object into its final orbit, from which time on no further guidance or control is possible or necessary. During this time, powerful radar stations on the ground are following the flight and checking that the object is on its proper path. Highly sensitive receiving stations are listening for the radio transmissions from the payload, accurately checking the frequency of these transmissions in order that the Doppler effect (change in apparent frequency with speed) may be used to check the velocity of the rocket as each

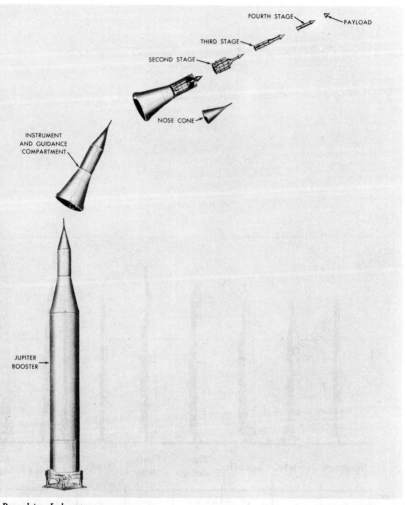

FOURTH STAGE · PAYLOAD

THIRD STAGE

SECOND STAGE

NOSE CONE

INSTRUMENT
AND GUIDANCE
COMPARTMENT

JUPITER
BOOSTER

Fig. 6. The Juno-Pioneer staging system.

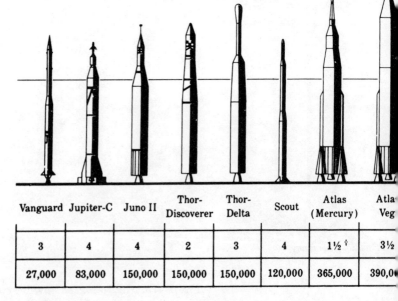

Vanguard	Jupiter-C	Juno II	Thor-Discoverer	Thor-Delta	Scout	Atlas (Mercury)	Atla Veg
3	4	4	2	3	4	1½ †	3½
27,000	83,000	150,000	150,000	150,000	120,000	365,000	390,0

Fortune Magazine and Jet Propulsion Laboratory

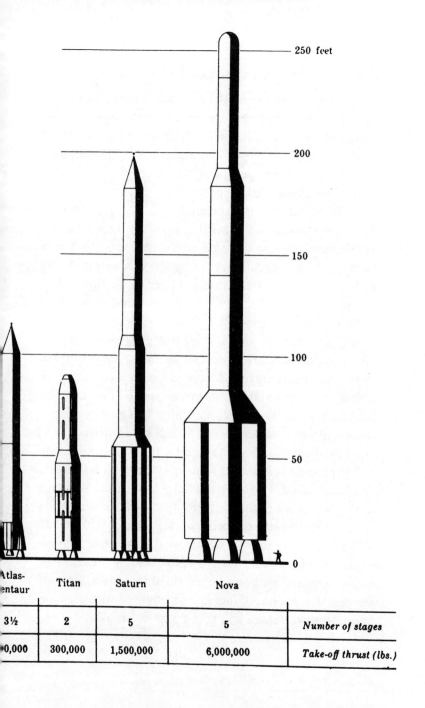

3½	2	5	5	*Number of stages*
0,000	300,000	1,500,000	6,000,000	*Take-off thrust (lbs.)*

Atlas-Centaur   Titan   Saturn   Nova

Fig. 7. Rocket systems envisaged as of August 1959.

stage is fired. Finally, as the payload goes into orbit (if it does), at various places around the earth huge receiving antennas, 90 feet in diameter, listen for the telemetering transmissions and record on hundreds or thousands of feet of recording paper the signals received so that they can be later analyzed. (Fig. 8.)

As one contemplates the enormous complexity of all this equipment and realizes that possibly the failure of a single transistor or a single soldered connection may ruin the whole operation, causing the valuable rocket to falter and requiring the safety officer to destroy it, it is not hard to understand why there are many failures for each successful flight.

The accuracy required of all this guidance and control equipment is also astonishing. If the final payload is projected in a direction even a few degrees above or below the horizontal, it will not attain the desired orbit and may go into a trajectory which brings it back into the earth's atmosphere where it will be destroyed.

Also, if the velocity attained by the object falls only a few percent below that required, the orbit will again not be attained. The question naturally arises: Why not add a few more pounds of fuel to the rocket motor so that one will be *sure* the proper final velocity is attained? When one remembers, however, that it may take a thousand pounds of fuel in a typical rocket of present-day design to place *one* pound of payload into orbit, one can see that the amount of fuel must be figured with extreme care; otherwise there will be no payload at all.

Fig. 8. Radio tracking antenna, Goldstone Lake, operated by Jet Propulsion Laboratory.

One thousand pounds of fuel for one pound of payload! That is a figure worthy of contemplation and explains in a single phrase why the launching of our satellites is such a difficult task. An enormous amount of energy is required. Incidentally, of the total energy required to get a payload into an orbit at, say, 200 miles above the earth, only one-tenth of the energy is needed to *lift* the object to that height and the other nine-tenths goes into the kinetic energy of the object itself.

It will greatly aid our future discussions if we insert at this point a brief discussion of the theory of the motion of an object in an orbit around an attracting body. To be specific, we consider a satellite in an orbit around the earth.

Such orbits in general are ellipses, as was discovered by Johannes Kepler, but one special case of an ellipse— namely, a circle—is simpler to treat and will serve our purpose.

The condition for a stable circular orbit around the earth is that the gravitational acceleration of the object toward the center of the earth shall be just equal to the required centripetal acceleration. The centripetal acceleration is always V^2/R where V is the velocity and R is the distance to the center of the earth. The gravitational acceleration near the earth is g (32 ft. per sec.^{2}), but this acceleration falls off inversely as R^2. Thus we have

$$\frac{V^2}{R} = g \ (R_o/R)^2$$

where R_o is the radius of the earth, or

$$V = \sqrt{gR_o} \; \sqrt{R_o/R}$$

This becomes, on inserting known values of g and R_o,

$$V = 26{,}000 \sqrt{R_o/R} \text{ ft. per second.} \qquad (1)$$

Often it is more convenient to deal with the time required for the object to make one complete orbit around the earth rather than with its linear speed. Since the circumference of the orbit is $2\pi R$, the period T is equal to $\frac{2\pi R}{V}$. Substituting in the value for V we get

$$T = \frac{2\pi R}{\sqrt{gR_o} \sqrt{R_o/R}}$$

which reduces to

$$T = 84 \, (R/R_o)^{3/2} \text{ minutes}$$

Thus we see at once that for any circular orbit at a given radius R both the velocity and the period are fixed. You can easily amuse yourselves by verifying that for an orbit near the surface of the earth—that is, for R equal to about R_o or 3,970 miles—the period is 84 minutes and the velocity about 26,000 feet per second, or 17,600 miles per hour. (Obviously such an orbit is impossible because of air friction. At 200 miles height the period is 86 minutes.) If we go to twice that distance from the center of the earth—that is, to a distance of 4,000 miles above the earth's surface—then $R_o/R = \frac{1}{2}$ and the velocity is 16,800 feet per second, and the period 240 minutes, or 4 hours. Finally, for an orbit 26,248 miles above the center of the earth (22,289 miles above the earth's surface) it turns out that the period is exactly 24 hours, and the velocity 6,872 miles per hour.

The situation for elliptical orbits is slightly more complex since, of course, the velocity then varies, decreasing as the object gets farther from the center of the earth and increasing again as it gets nearer. The velocity equation becomes

$$V = 26,000 \sqrt{\frac{2R_o}{R} - \frac{R_o}{a}} \qquad (3)$$

and the period

$$T = 84 \, (a/R_o)^{3/2} \qquad (4)$$

where *a* is the semi-major axis of the ellipse. According to the laws discovered by Kepler, the period is independent of the shape of the orbit and depends only upon its longest axis. Thus, as we have seen, a circular orbit of radius of 26,000 miles or diameter of 52,000 miles would have a period of 24 hours, and any elliptical orbit of the same major axis of 52,000 miles would also have a 24-hour period.

The moon's orbit (since it is nearly circular) can be computed from equation 1 or 2. Its distance is about 240,000 miles from the earth and it can be verified that the period comes out to be 28 days.

This simple mathematics is all we need to tell us some interesting things about motions and the orbits. Let us imagine, for example, some future situation in which two satellites, with a man riding in each, are traveling in precisely the same orbit around the earth, say at a distance of 10,000 miles above the surface. One rider discovers that he is 100 miles behind his friend and would like to catch up. This will require that he have some jet motors and jet fuel aboard. His natural inclination, of course, would be simply to use his jet equipment to give him a little extra speed. But now he finds himself traveling at a speed too great for that orbit. The extra centrifugal force, therefore, will cause the satellite to rise to a higher orbit; but in a higher orbit it must go at a lower speed (as R increases, V decreases). In technical terms the potential energy has been increased and the kinetic energy has been decreased. Our pilot finds himself, therefore, not catching up with his friend but actually falling farther behind him.

However, he is on to the tricks now and he gives his retro-jet a blast which will slow him down. This will, of course, cause him to fall off into a lower orbit where he will be moving with a *higher* speed. If the orbit is sufficiently low, he will now catch up with his friend but will not be in the same orbit with him and will pass him a few miles below. If now he's real clever he can speed himself up again, thereby rising to the same orbit as his friend and at the same time slowing down to the same speed. If he has miscalculated and finds himself a little ahead or behind, he will have to repeat the process.

This simple example will let you see the absurdity of many of the discussions you hear about space platforms. I think the speculations which used to be prevalent about stationary platforms "anchored in space" are no longer heard, for, obviously, a stationary platform is impossible in the vicinity of any attracting body such as the earth or the sun. The nearest approach to a stationary platform is one in our 26,000-mile orbit, with a 24-hour period, equal to the earth's rotational speed. Such an object will *appear* stationary *if* the orbit is exactly circular, if exactly the right height, and if exactly over the earth's equator. But it is traveling at 6,800 miles per hour, and is not something you can easily hop on and off of like a slow streetcar.

As one other example we might consider an object which we want to shoot to the vicinity of the moon and then bring back. This means there must be established an elliptical orbit whose major axis is some 240,000 miles long. Our equation tells us that the time required to circumnavigate such an orbit is very nearly 10 days. This means it would take 5 days to go out and 5 days to return, and nothing you can do will get you out to the moon *and bring you back* in any less time than 10 days. If you start off with a higher velocity you would get *to* the moon faster, but then your ellipse would extend far beyond the moon and by the time the longer orbit had been completed the return time would be more than 10 days. We are assuming here, of course, that we don't get close enough to the moon so that the moon's attraction itself seriously distorts the orbit. (See Fig. 9.)

It has sometimes been assumed that if an object is projected into an orbit that brings it close to the moon —without striking it—the moon might then capture the object into an orbit about itself. This, however, cannot

TYPICAL MOON PROBE TRAJECTORIES

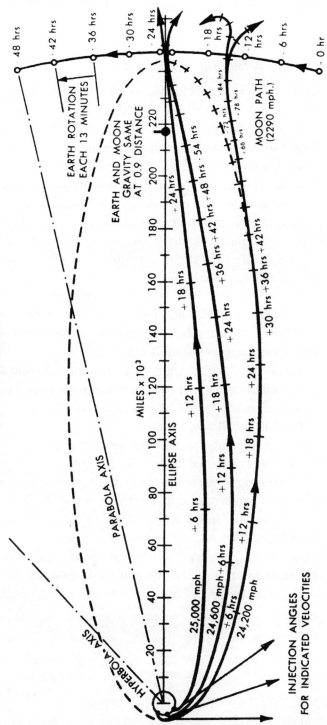

Jet Propulsion Laboratory

Fig. 9. Possible orbits to the vicinity of the moon.

happen. The moon's field might violently affect the orbit, but an object coming into the moon's field with a finite velocity will always have enough energy to escape. With respect to the moon the orbit must be nearly hyperbolic.

However, when the object gets well within the moon's influence, if it is suddenly slowed down by a retro-rocket blast, then, if we have been clever about it, a permanent orbit about the moon may be achieved. This is a fond hope of the space scientists, for such a "lunar moon"— a moon around the moon—would have a host of important scientific missions.

Because of technical problems, however, the first lunar probes will be—and have been—designed to sail near the moon and return, or else to sail past the moon and on into space, or to hit it hard.

Where will an object go which is shot out from the earth (whether it goes near the moon or not) and then escapes from the earth's gravitational field?

We must recall two things.

1. After leaving the earth behind, our object is still in the sun's gravitational field.

2. Although the escaping object may come to move very slowly with respect to the earth, it is still endowed with the earth's speed around the sun—some 19 miles per second.

Therefore, if the earth, moving at 19 miles per second, is held in an orbit of about 186 million miles diameter, so will our "escaping" vehicle also pass automatically into a similar orbit about the sun—and will have a similar period of about one year.

Pioneer IV, launched March 3, 1959, was the first U.S. probe to achieve escape from the earth and become a small earthlike planet, or "asteroid." Actually, since it attained a speed of some 1.3 miles per second above the escape speed and in a direction slightly toward the sun, its orbit is more elliptical than the earth's orbit; its major axis is 198 million miles and its period 395 days. (Fig. 10.) It will take twelve years for the earth to gain one full lap on Pioneer IV in their race around the sun.

In some of the earlier satellite launching systems each pound of payload required 3,000 pounds of total rocket weight—mostly, of course, in fuel. Hence, over 3,000 pounds of thrust was also required to lift the rocket from the ground. Later designs brought this down to 1,000 and then to a few hundred pounds thrust for each pound of payload, and a reasonable limit of 100 pounds of thrust per pound of payload is now in sight. Even with the most perfect design, chemical fuels cannot do better than 50 pounds per pound.

The kinetic energy (plus the potential energy) of one pound of payload in an earth orbit is far less than the energy of combustion of 100 pounds of fuel and oxidant. It turns out, in fact, that over 98 percent of the heat of combustion goes into the kinetic energy of the escaping propellent gases and of the discarded structures, while less than 2 percent goes into the kinetic energy of the final payload. This is a heavy price to pay for kinetic energy—but that is the price-tag which nature has set and there is no way to avoid it. The so-called "exotic" propulsion methods all require even more energy than chemical combustion—and also usually a more expensive form of energy (such as fission energy). Incidentally, the main advantage of fission energy in, say, a submarine (i.e., no refueling) is absent in a rocket, for the propulsion material to eject must be carried along anyway.

The simple energetics of orbit calculations (equation 3) reveals an interesting point worth remembering. It is this: In any stable circular orbit about an attracting center the kinetic energy is exactly half the kinetic energy required to escape from that orbit. That is, if $a = R$

$$V = 26,000 \sqrt{R_o/R}.$$

But if $a = \infty$

$$V = 26,000 \sqrt{2R_o/R}.$$

Since kinetic energy is proportional to V^2, the energy is twice as great in the second case.

An earth satellite, for example, in a circular orbit near the earth (just above the atmosphere) would have a velocity of 17,700 miles per hour. Multiplying this by $\sqrt{2}$ we see that at a velocity of about 25,000 miles per hour the satellite would escape from the earth's pull entirely.

As previously mentioned, a vehicle which has escaped from the earth still participates in the earth's rotational velocity of 19 miles per second around the sun. Again, to

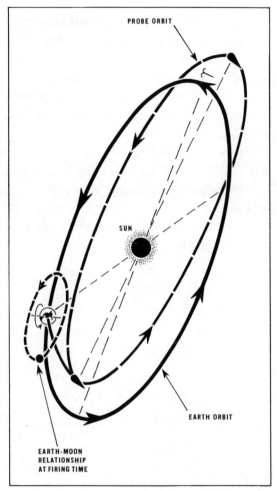

PROBE ORBIT

SUN

EARTH ORBIT

EARTH-MOON
RELATIONSHIP
AT FIRING TIME

Jet Propulsion Laboratory

Fig. 10. Orbit of Pioneer IV around the sun.

escape from the sun from a position in the earth's orbit requires increasing that velocity by the $\sqrt{2}$, or 1.4 times, to about 26 miles per second. That represents 25 times as much kinetic energy as for an earth orbit—which is the reason that journeying to the outer planets is difficult, even when half the energy has already been supplied by the motion of the earth itself.

Thus we see that many of the technological problems of launching space vehicles have been solved. But some imposing difficulties remain before all our space dreams can be achieved. Next we shall ask about what we put *in* the space vehicles we launch and what are some of the goals and purposes of our first space ventures.

II
The Space Laboratory

IN THE EARLY days of the space age no one cared much what was in the satellite as long as it got into orbit and carried a radio transmitter so it could be tracked for a while. However, the process of hurling dead weights into space is a pretty useless enterprise, and so all satellites have contained some kind of instrumentation for making observations and reporting them back to earth. More and more, as costs and sizes mount, we will be forced to ask what the payload is for and why its trip is necessary.

What, then, can one do with a vehicle in space—other than just send it along for a ride?

Most people appear to think of a space vehicle as, first of all, a military device, and they suppose that when a war begins space vehicles will be full of atomic bombs. However, no one has thought up a convincing reason for putting a nuclear bomb into an orbit around the earth—where it is quite certain *not* to do anybody any harm. A rocket-propelled ICBM to put a bomb at some point on the earth is a useful device in time of war. But because the same rocket can be used as a booster to put an object into space does not mean that space objects themselves have any lethal value. The problem is, if you do have a bomb in a satellite, how do you get it back to earth at the right place?

Of course, military people are also interested in non-lethal devices and would like to use space vehicles for observation of the terrain and the weather, and also for communications. But these are civilian uses also. So we may assume that most of the interesting uses of satellites and space probes are essentially civilian—or at least nonlethal. We will leave out such chimeric schemes as transporting soldiers to the moon—for purposes not specified. If they are just going there to launch weapons back at the earth, I can think of cheaper and more accurate ways of accomplishing that.

What, then, would it be interesting to do with a space vehicle?

Aside from carrying passengers and freight and aside from serving as a communication relay, a satellite is, first and last, primarily an observation post. When equipped with the proper instruments it can make observations of many kinds of phenomena not observable from the earth, and then transmit them back to earth.

The things we may want to observe fall conveniently into three categories:

1. *Things related to the earth:* its clouds and weather patterns; its electric, magnetic, and gravitational fields; the ionosphere and any other layers of charged particles attached to it.

2. *Things related to space itself:* radiations traversing space from whatever source and of whatever nature, electromagnetic or corpuscular; residual matter present (for space is not really empty after all—its density is simply very low), whether the matter be atomic or molecular, fine dust or pebbles, stones or rocks of various sizes (micro-meteorites or meteorites).

3. *Things related to other objects in space:* the moon, the planets, and the stars—which can better be observed from a space vehicle than from the earth, either because the vehicle can get much closer (as to the moon), or simply because, being above the atmosphere, it can get a better view, e.g., of the stars and galaxies. Eventually, a direct landing on the moon or a planet can be achieved for more direct observation of those objects.

When one starts listing all the scientific observations one would like to carry out in these categories, one gets an imposing list indeed—especially when one lists all the experiments he would like to do when he gets *on* the moon or Mars or Venus. There is enough to keep us busy for centuries to come—if Congress continues to appropriate the money.

Before taking up these experiments in detail, let us examine one problem that keeps cropping up and is common to all space observations—the problem of getting the information back home. A Geiger counter ticking away merrily 10,000 miles above the earth is of no "earthly use" unless it can get the data back to earth. Similarly, a fine astronomical photograph riding around the earth in a satellite is equally useless. We must either physically transfer the picture from satellite to earth, or else reduce it to electrical form and transmit it by radio. In either case we face troubles.

For instance, it is a majestically challenging task to eject a photographic film from a satellite and have it reach home base safely. Going out or coming back, undeveloped film would get a thorough fogging from the Van Allen radiation, of course. But even if we could solve this problem, the fact remains that we do not know any practical method of getting a satellite package back to earth with a reasonable chance of recovering it safely.

I remind you that an object cannot be dropped from a satellite; it will sail right along with the satellite. It must be quite forcibly ejected with the right velocity and direction to enter a trajectory which will strike the right place on the earth. The package must be able to survive the plunge through the atmosphere without getting too warm to melt the emulsion. And you must be able to find it! So we will let future generations struggle with that one. (There have already been three unsuccessful recovery experiments, and in no case do we have the faintest idea where the object landed. You see why I am skeptical about accurate bombing.)

The radio transmission scheme sounds more attractive, and indeed it has worked splendidly in the satellites already launched. But there are problems here too. If our vehicle stays near the earth so that .01 watt of radio power is enough to transmit the necessary data (as in the first Explorer satellites), and if we wish to transmit for only a few hours or a few days, ordinary electric dry cells will supply the power. In Pioneer IV the transmitted power was .18 watt and it was heard out to 400,000 miles, but the batteries failed after 82 hours. Had they not failed, the signals could have been heard to 700,000 miles. Yet, Pioneer IV transmitted only fairly simple information—nothing as complex as a photograph. The power requirement increases as the information rate goes up. Also, the power required for a given signal increases as the square of the distance. If .18 watt was enough for 700,000 miles, to get the same signal at twice the distance, or at 1,400,000 miles, would take 4 times the power, or .72 watt; at 7,000,000 miles, 100 times the power, or 18 watts; at the distance of Mars' closest approach, 40,000,000 miles, some 600 watts; and at Mars' farthest distance, 240,000,000 miles, 21.6 kilowatts. This is power *radiated;* the power *supplied* must be much greater. Obviously, dry cells trying to supply kilowatts of power would not last long or would be a pretty heavy load. To be specific, it would take 9 tons of batteries to supply 1 kilowatt for one month. And for long journeys the power would be needed for many months or years, not for just a few hours or days. To conserve power we will have to put directive antennas on the satellite if we can invent a way to keep them pointed at the earth. Most importantly, we will have to use very narrow band-width transmission, and then be restricted to transmitting information very slowly. Ordinary television requiring a very wide band is clearly out of the question for distant journeys, at least for the present.

There are, of course, ways of generating electrical power within the satellite itself rather than using batteries. We could use chemical fuel, such as that used in a gasoline-driven generator, but this would require large amounts of fuel and oxygen. A nuclear reactor could be used; it has the advantage of long life and needs no oxygen; but the reactor itself and the heat exchange equipment, turbine and generator, are very heavy. They will, no doubt, be practical at some future time when very large long-life space vehicles come into use. The generation of electric power by a thermocouple, heated by a radioactive material, is also possible—but is also extremely expensive and is limited by the half-life of the radioactivity, generally a few weeks or months. All of these methods for converting heat energy into electric energy also require a device for radiating away the waste heat in order to maintain the required temperature difference. But a good radiating surface will also be an efficient absorber of heat from the sun and so must be kept turned away from the sun by some sort of automatic equipment.

The most promising answer seems to lie in the use of solar energy. This has already been successful in two satellites (Fig. 11), and has the advantage of working for an indefinite period without fuel and requires no generator or other moving parts. A good solar cell can deliver 100 watts of power for each square meter of absorbing area.

Fig. 11. The Explorer VI satellite, showing vanes carrying solar batteries.

Some improvement in efficiency will no doubt be achieved, but, at best, solar radiation will have to be collected by at least a square meter of area for each kilowatt produced. As one gets closer to the sun, as in a journey to Venus, this power yield increases. But in going to Mars the sun's radiation falls to less than half the intensity at the earth. Also, for journeys near the earth, the satellite will be in the earth's shadow up to one-half of the time and the equipment must stop running, or else storage batteries will be needed to carry on through the night.

So far we have talked only of power needed to operate the radio transmitter. Obviously the large future long-range space probes will carry a large amount of other equipment which will require power also. Hundreds or even thousands of kilowatts would be required for some of the more elaborate vehicles which have been suggested—and for those which propose television transmitters (with band-widths of many megacycles) the radio power alone could be thousands of kilowatts.

All in all, the furnishing of energy to activate all the equipment aboard a large or long-range space vehicle poses one of the most baffling problems in the entire technology of space research. There is nothing impossible in principle about carrying along a supply of chemical or nuclear fuel and the associated generating equipment, and nothing impossible about extracting energy from the sun. But the technical problems of long life, reliability, low weight, and automatic control have not been fully solved for the case of very long journeys to great distances.

But while engineers are working away at this problem, scientists are busy designing the equipment they would like to send into space to make important scientific observations when and if the energy is available. Scientific interest in space was enormously heightened by the discovery of the Van Allen layers of charged particles, which proved that there were new and unexpected things to be discovered out there. It will be interesting to examine the Van Allen experiments in some detail.

In the early planning of the scientific experiments to be carried out in the satellites to be launched in connection with the International Geophysical Year it was agreed that the measurement of cosmic rays at great heights would be of great interest. Dr. James A. Van Allen of the State University of Iowa had been measuring cosmic rays and other upper-atmospheric phenomena from balloons and rockets for a number of years. He was able to extrapolate his measurements to estimate the intensity of cosmic rays in space a few hundred miles above the earth.

Dr. Van Allen proposed that one of the IGY satellites carry a Geiger counter designed to measure cosmic rays outside the atmosphere and transmit the counting rate by radio back to earth. This experiment was duly scheduled for one of the Vanguard series of satellites. But Vanguard was delayed, and the news of Sputnik I initiated an accelerated program to get a U.S. satellite into orbit. As has already been told, the Army Ballistic Missile Agency and the Jet Propulsion Laboratory of Caltech were assigned the job of using a Jupiter-C to launch a scientific payload. The Van Allen counter equipment was ideally suited to the Explorer vehicle and it was chosen for the first shot—thus becoming the first U.S. scientific space experiment. It was a lucky coincidence. For, to everyone's astonishment, the Geiger counter, instead of clicking along at a leisurely rate as had been expected, increased its counting rate at high altitudes and actually became paralyzed. Its behavior was indeed a great puzzle at first since, while paralyzed, it provided no data at all and we thought it had broken down. Later on, as the satellite came back to low altitudes, the counter started working again. Not until Explorers III and IV had made flights with more refined equipment was the story put together, and it took Pioneers III and IV to complete the astonishing picture. It is now clear that, as we move away from the earth's atmosphere, the radiation measured by a Geiger counter is at first the rather weak radiation of the well-known cosmic rays. At a few hundred miles height above the equator, however, the counting rate begins to rise rapidly, and at an altitude of 3,000 miles reaches a peak value over 1,000 times greater than the cosmic rays. The intensity then falls to a minimum at 6,000 miles, then rises rapidly again to a much higher peak of 100,000 times cosmic rays at some 14,000 miles. Finally, as the Pioneer shots revealed, it falls off slowly and somewhat irregularly again, reaching the normal cosmic-ray value at about 60,000 miles.

Detailed analysis shows there are two belts of charged particles around the earth, bent down toward the magnetic poles and rising to great heights above the equator. (Fig. 12) Measurements with a counter shielded by a layer of lead one-eighth of an inch thick showed that, while in the lower belt the particles penetrated this shield easily, almost none of the particles in the upper belt got through. It is supposed by some that the lower belt consists of high-energy protons, trapped by the earth's field, possibly having their origin in the decay of neutrons produced in the upper atmosphere by impinging high-energy cosmic rays. The upper layer is thought to be a cloud of electrons coming from the sun, also trapped by the magnetic field. Within the period of three months between Pioneers III and IV, the intensity of the upper layer apparently increased eight times. A series of solar flares had occurred in that period. It is possible that ejected electrons from the sun had been trapped for a few weeks before "leaking out" of the "bottle" created by the magnetic lines of force converging at the magnetic poles.

But there are many mysteries still to be solved, and it is hoped that the present Explorer VI (in an orbit extending out to heights of 26,000 miles), whose solar-powered equipment should operate for the year or more while the satellite remains in orbit, will answer many of the puzzling questions.

The answers are relatively important if we ever expect

to send a man aloft in a space vehicle. In an unshielded container a man would be exposed to the x-rays produced by the impact of the particles on the case, and these might amount to between 10 and 100 roentgens per hour. The "maximum safe dose" has been set for humans at .1 roentgen per day, or .3 roentgen in any week. The lethal dose is about 600 roentgens. Men will have to go through the belts quickly, or remain under them or over them, or else carry bulky shielding—all very unattractive alternatives.

Thus, the very first space instruments achieved a startling discovery. What will be the next? Here are some things that scientists would like to examine:

Things related to the earth

1. A very much more exhaustive exploration of the radiation clouds out to distances equal to the moon's orbit. What are these particles? How are they held in these belts? Where do they come from? How fast do they move and in what paths? How are they trapped in the earth's magnetic field?

2. What is the nature, strength, and extent of the earth's magnetic field, clear out to where it becomes inappreciable? Does its shape or strength reveal anything new about its origin? Better knowledge of the earth's field might help us make better predictions of the paths of cosmic-ray particles. Its variations and their relation to sunspots and other solar phenomena may tell us about the radiations coming to the earth from the sun.

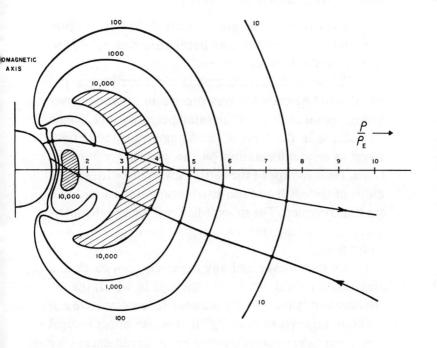

Jet Propulsion Laboratory

Fig. 12. The Van Allen charged particle clouds, showing the path of Pioneer III. The contours are lines of equal intensity. Distance (ρ) is measured relative to the radius of the earth (ρ_E).

What is the origin of magnetic storms? What is the precise relation to sunspots and flares? Are they related to changes in the Van Allen layers?

3. Can we make accurate plots of the earth's gravitational field? Already the very precise observations, over a long period of time, of the small perturbations from a true ellipse in the orbit of the Vanguard satellite have given us new information on the earth's gravity and, hence, on the shape of the earth. Any asymmetries in the shape of the earth and the distribution of mass within it are thus revealed. The moon's field will be equally interesting, as will the transition region between earth and moon fields.

4. We have never had any experience on earth in a gravitational field other than the one in which the acceleration of falling objects is about 32 feet/sec.[2] We can simulate higher values of "g" by the use of centrifugal force, but lower values cannot be achieved except for brief periods. At the same time, within any freely falling object such as a satellite or any free space vehicle, the gravitational and centrifugal accelerations cancel to give "zero g." What are the results in such an environment? Do clocks run slower, as predicted by the General Relativity Theory? (We must distinguish between the slowing up due to reduced gravity and the slowing up caused by the high velocity. By testing in several orbits with differing velocities—but all with zero g—the two effects can be separated.) There are scores of interesting physical, chemical and biological experiments we would like to perform at zero g.

5. What kind of an electrostatic field does the earth have, if any? That is, is the earth electrically charged? If so, positively or negatively, and how much? And why? The charged layers in the ionosphere and the Van Allen belts will produce local electrostatic fields. What are they like? We have almost no information on this subject.

6. As we look back at the earth from very great distances what do we see? This is a tough question to answer. We must either carry a man with a good visual memory and get him back, or we must carry aloft a pretty good television station to transmit back good pictures. These things are difficult—even if we did not have to worry about the Van Allen radiation. We would like very much to have good motion pictures, promptly and continuously, of the earth's cloud cover and the storm patterns. But we are not going to get them soon. Sometime later they will come, and the interest of the meteorologists and others will be great. It is rather premature, however, to be assuring the American people that "control of the weather" from satellites is just around the corner.

7. The military people would like to use a satellite to find out what the Russians are doing. The difficulties suggested above still apply—plus the additional one that to get sharp pictures which will reveal anything useful introduces difficult problems in optics, photography, stabilization of the camera, transmission of the pictures back after a delay to give the satellite time to return to a point over a home base, etc. It is all scientifically pos-

sible, of course—it is just a very tough job for the engineers! And shall the camera take continuous pictures— millions per day covering the whole earth? If so, how do you store them? Still worse, who looks at them? It appears as though this is one case where we must take a man along to snap the shutter only when there is something worth seeing.

8. And the last point leads us to conclude that, since at some future date it will really be useful—and not just spectacular—to put men into space, we should soon start some careful systematic experiments to see how men might be affected and what it takes to keep them alive and alert—and to get them *back* alive—most of the time. However spectacular it may be to put a man in space, let us remember that unless he can really contribute something that instruments cannot do, we should leave him safely and inexpensively at home.

Things related to space itself

1. Space is a veritable sea of radiations. High- and low-speed charged particles traverse it, coming from the sun, from outside the solar system, possibly from distant galaxies. A few of the particles penetrate the earth's magnetic field and its atmosphere; many more do not. There is much to be learned about them. There are electromagnetic radiations too—radio waves, infrared, visible and ultraviolet light waves, x-rays, gamma rays— coming from all over the universe. Again most of them fail to penetrate our atmosphere, but a few do and we

see them with our radio and optical telescopes. Soon we can observe the radiation directly, undamaged by contact with the atmosphere.

2. There is a good deal of matter in space, too. In our solar system there may be an average of one thousand atoms every cubic centimeter. That is a vacuum a million times better than we can produce on earth. There are also molecules, dust particles, and chunks of rock. The latter we would like to avoid, for to capture them would be pretty risky, moving as they are at speeds of many miles per second. But we would like to examine this interplanetary matter and see what it is. Are there organic molecules present in space? If so, how come?

3. The sun apparently ejects clouds of matter—charged and uncharged particles—into space every now and then, on the occasion of solar flares. How do these clouds travel through space? Are they swirling clouds, and thus accompanied by magnetic fields? Are they indeed "attached" to the sun by magnetic lines of force which stretch out as they move? Is it these magnetic "winds" that disturb the earth's magnetic field? Speculations on these subjects are extraordinarily interesting—but, without experimental measurements, a bit abstruse.

Things related to other objects in space

The sun, the moon, the planets and the stars have always been objects of continuing interest to men, and they are the special subjects of study by the astronomers. They now take on renewed interest for two reasons: the moon and the nearer planets will soon be reached directly by our instruments and later by human observers; and instruments at various points in space, above our atmosphere, will be able to make far clearer observations of even the most distant galaxies than will ever be possible within our blanket of air.

Let us list first a few of the items of scientific interest which will be susceptible to direct observation or contact. Only the moon, Venus, and Mars fall into this category for the foreseeable future—and many observations on even these nearby objects present formidable difficulties. We would like information about the following items relating to each of these objects, though we shall defer detailed discussion to the next lecture:

1. *The atmosphere:* The moon has none; yet some imaginative newspaper writers gave vivid descriptions of the "echoing crash" of Lunik striking the moon. (There is no sound in a vacuum.) The atmosphere of Venus is completely opaque, and that of Mars contains carbon dioxide. But what is the full story?

2. *The surface:* Even for the moon, whose every geographic detail (on this side) is known and even named, we do not know the nature of the surface. About Mars we know very little, and about the invisible Venus surface, nothing at all. Land or water, mountains or valleys, rock or dust—what?

3. *Internal structure:* Is there a crust, a mantel, and a core like the earth—or something else? A seismographic survey could eventually tell the story.

4. *The shape:* The flattening at the poles, as related to the speed of spin, tells interesting facts about the history and structure. Mars appears flatter than it should be from its spin. Why? Uranus has an axis of spin in the plane of its orbit. Why?

5. *Chemical composition:* Do the elements appear in the same abundance as on the earth and in similar chemical compounds? Theories of the origin and evolution of the solar system and of the universe need this information.

6. *Magnetic fields:* Are there any about the moon and planets? If so, how strong? How is the magnetic axis related to the axis of spin? How are incoming cosmic rays affected? The Russian Lunik reported no lunar magnetic field. This leads to interesting conclusions.

7. *Ionized layers:* Are there ionospheres or Van Allen layers of ionized particles? If so, then we wish to know all about them. Jupiter occasionally emits radiation of radio wavelengths. Why? Are there thunderstorms? Or high-altitude ionic turbulence?

8. *Is there life?* To most men this is the most absorbing question of all. Are there viruses, or bacteria, or spores, or simple plants, or even higher forms of life on Venus or Mars? No one can still insist with certainty that the earth is unique in harboring living things, but it might be—at least in our solar system. We would give a great deal to find even one bacterium which is native to Mars.

The list could be indefinitely prolonged. All the things

we are still studying about the earth we would like to know about the planets. We will have whole new sciences of geography, geology, oceanography (?), meteorology, seismology, possibly biology, etc.

As we look to more distant objects in space which we cannot yet (or ever) reach but will be able to see more clearly, we realize that a wholly new era in astronomy is dawning. Up to the present, practically all our knowledge of the universe is gleaned from the particular radiations that can penetrate our atmosphere. Now, suddenly, every wavelength in the electromagnetic spectrum, from the shortest gamma rays to the longest radio waves, becomes accessible to use as an observational tool. In some wavelength regions we may find nothing—but others, such as the far ultraviolet, are sure to be rich in new information.

A complete astronomical observatory in space—equipped for measurements at all wavelengths—is still a far-distant dream. But already high altitude rockets have revealed some new things, and even very crude and simple measurements in certain cases will be of great value. To cite one example: The principal wavelength radiated by hydrogen gas (which has been excited and is returning to its normal state) is the Lyman-alpha line in the far ultraviolet (1216 A.U.). The sun—and most other stars, too—must give out such radiation in great abundance. We badly need the "portrait" of hydrogen which the study of this light will reveal.

Yes, space is an interesting place in which to do research. No wonder the physicists, chemists, geologists, meteorologists, and astronomers, as well as the biologists and engineers, are interested.

III
The Solar System

IT IS QUITE POSSIBLE—some would say it is quite probable—that millions of stars in our Milky Way and millions of stars in other galaxies are, like our sun, equipped with an array of nonluminous planets which revolve about them. But we cannot be sure—and we have no assurance that we shall ever possess instruments capable of seeing such planets even if they exist about the very nearest stars.

But whether our planetary system is unique or not, it is of vast interest to us as human beings. For, on one of these planets we live. Also the solar system as a whole constitutes the one tiny corner of the universe which we can hope actually to explore and to become intimately acquainted with.

Strangely enough, not much attention has been paid to the solar system by astronomers in recent years. The stars and galaxies are of much more fascinating interest to a scientist equipped with a modern telescope. And the breathtaking advances that have been made in our concepts of the universe and our theories of cosmology more than justify this fascination. But, since now we may someday be going to the moon or Venus or Mars, it behooves us to take a closer look at our near neighbors. Far more careful study of these objects with instruments on the earth would be useful—and might save vast effort and expense in certain space ventures. There are some questions, however, that can be answered only by direct contact.

Let us see what we do know about our three near neighbors—the moon, Venus, and Mars—and then see what space research may add.

The moon

Astronomically speaking, the moon is a small but intensely interesting object. It is the earth's only satellite, rotating about the earth once in 27 days, 7 hours, 43 minutes, and 11.5 seconds at an average distance of 238,857 miles from the earth's center. Actually, of course, the moon and earth rotate like an unsymmetrical dumbbell about their common center of mass which, since the earth is 81.25 times the mass of the moon, is 81.25 times closer to the center of the earth than to the center of the moon. This puts the point well inside the earth's surface but some 2,900 miles from its center.

The moon has a diameter of a little over one-fourth that of the earth, and the acceleration of gravity at its surface is about one-sixth that at the earth's surface. This is too small a value to permit the moon to retain a gaseous atmosphere at the temperatures which exist, and without such a protecting blanket the surface of the moon gets very hot in the middle of its long "day" and radiates this heat away rapidly to space during the equally long "night." Thus, the day temperature is about 134° C. (272° F.), which is hotter than the normal earthly boiling point of water, while at night the temperature falls to −153° C. (−244° F.), which is approaching the normal boiling temperature of liquid air. The moon spins on its own axis at exactly the same rate as it rotates about the earth. This means we see always the same side. It means, too, that the moon's day is 28 earth-days long. At first sight the exact equality of these periods seems strange, but it is the normal tendency for all satellites to attain this state as spin energy is given up to tidal friction and, hence, to heat.

It is evident that much information about the moon (note the items listed in the preceding chaper) may be obtained from instrumented flights to the close vicinity of the moon and, eventually, with instruments landed on the moon. Nevertheless, to land men on the moon is an irresistible human urge—and they can also add immensely to our information-gathering ability. What kind of a place is the moon for human habitation?

Briefly, it's not good.

It has no free oxygen. That is extremely serious, of course, because a man needs about 1 to 1.5 pounds of oxygen every day.

It has no water. That is bad too, for a man takes in 1 to 2 pounds of water a day in normal earthly life.

It has, of course, no food.

Its "climate" is excessively bad. 272° F. is hot! Even at zero humidity the "discomfort index" would be pretty high. And −244° F. is cold! And without a protecting blanket of air, men will be subject to the whole spectrum of space radiations whose intensity in the ultraviolet and x-ray regions is quite unknown. A radiation "umbrella," which will not itself melt in the daytime or freeze to the shattering point at night, is a "must" for the moon man. When he carries this, along with a pressurized space suit and oxygen supply, plus all his other equipment, food, and fuel, he is bound to have quite a load to be lifted off the earth and landed gently on the moon. Furthermore, unlike an instrument package, a man must have equipment and fuel to return home. And this must be lifted from the earth too. Thus, to lift 2,000 pounds from the earth would take a thrust of 600,000 pounds. But to add 2 pounds of fuel required to land each pound gently on the moon means 6,000 pounds to be lifted from the earth. That requires 1,800,000 pounds of thrust. Add a pound of fuel to lift each pound off the moon (doubling the thrust again to 3,600,000 pounds), and one more pound to land gently on the earth, and we get 7,200,000 pounds of thrust as the total requirement.

The first ventures to the moon, then, will be with instruments that do not have to come back and which do not need food, water, and oxygen. They do need electric power, however. And if they are to study the moon's terrain, analyze the materials of its surface, take and transmit pictures of various portions of the surface, test the materials for radioactivity, and hunt for signs of rudimentary life, then automatic instruments, partially controlled from the earth, of unbelievable complexity and dependable reliability must be developed. The colossal cost of sending probes to land on the moon cannot be justified unless there is a large and not a small chance that the instruments will, for the most part, achieve their intended missions.

Nevertheless, sober-minded scientists and engineers (more scientists than engineers, I fear) believe that these things can be accomplished in the next decade, and development work is now proceeding.

The moon is a body of exceptionally great interest to those scientists interested in the origin and evolution of the solar system—and of the universe in general. The moon is, in a true sense, an unspoiled relic of the days when the solar system was being formed. (Fig. 13) No processes of erosion by wind or water, of decomposition or decay, no alterations due to the growth or death of plant or animal life have taken place. Only a steady bombardment by meteors, and possibly some volcanic activity, have changed the moon's surface from what it was 4.5 billion years ago. It would be enormously revealing to have some samples of the moon to analyze—uranium-lead ratios to obtain age data, crystal structure samples to learn of the thermal history. One proposal for a lunar package lists thirty experiments which should be done to obtain information needed to learn of the moon's composition, structure, and history. It is claimed

Fig. 13. Southern portion of the moon at last quarter, showing the region from Ptolmaeus to the limb. Taken with 100-inch telescope.

that all these instruments—including chemical analyzers, x-ray fluorescence equipment, neutron-scattering equipment, seismographic and magnetic equipment, together with a roving vehicle to transport the equipment from place to place on the lunar surface—can be built with a total weight of under 1,000 pounds and a total power supply, excluding radio transmitter, of under 1 kilowatt. This is, no doubt, an optimistic estimate—possibly very optimistic—but it is made by instrumentation engineers with some experience.

At any rate, lunar soft landings carrying much useful instrumentation will be feasible in five years or so, and at last we will begin to know our solar system from direct examination. It is hoped that new and intensive studies of the moon with the best of the modern astronomical instruments can be undertaken promptly to provide data needed by those planning the probe experiments.

And, of course, before a soft landing on the moon, it would be possible to establish a satellite in an orbit about the moon, securing information from a few hundred miles above the moon's surface. This, incidentally, is more difficult than a direct "hard" hit on the moon.

Eventually, of course, a lunar observatory—manned or unmanned—will be of enormous scientific value for measuring cosmic rays, corpuscular radiation from the sun and other regions, radio, optical, and x-ray radiations from all heavenly objects—undistorted and unfiltered by any atmosphere or, presumably, by any appreciable magnetic field. But this is a more distant dream. Maybe men will not be able to survive on the moon at all! But if men do land on the moon, let us hope they will know some geology and chemistry so they can send back useful reports of what they see.

Venus

Venus is the planet which comes closest to the earth—minimum, about 26 million miles—and yet it is one about which we have very little information. There are two chief reasons for this:

1. When Venus is closest, it is between (or nearly between) the earth and the sun and so it cannot be seen in the sun's glare. As it moves away from the sun's disc it is illuminated only at one edge, like a new moon, and not much of its surface can be seen. (Fig. 14) At maximum separation from the sun in the sky, it is still only a "half moon" and it is now some 65 million miles away. When Venus is "full" it is close to or behind the sun. Obviously observations are difficult!

2. Venus' surface is completely hidden from view by a dense atmosphere whose thickness and composition are unknown (only carbon dioxide has been detected). It is not known whether Venus rotates on its axis like the earth, or always presents the same face to the sun (as does Mercury). Whether Venus' surface is a vast ocean or a vast desert, or something else, is quite unknown. The temperature of the outer portion of the atmosphere is $-39°$ C. and radio measurements which can penetrate down into the atmosphere, possibly to the surface, give a

temperature of between 200° and 400° C. This would suggest that the atmosphere is of such a nature as to give an excellent "greenhouse effect"—i.e., heat can get in but not out. The earth, if moved with its atmosphere to the Venus orbit, would rise in temperature from the present 20° C. (68° F.) to only 69° C. (155° F.). In any case, the surface of Venus could be a rather hot place by earthly standards. Perhaps, if there is lots of water on the planet, if might be largely in the form of vapor which at the outermost part of the atmosphere is frozen into ice crystals. This might account for the "whiteness" of the planet. No water vapor has been detected spectroscopically, however, and this would be expected if it were frozen. Only carbon dioxide has been definitely observed—but the theory that the clouds are tiny crystals of "dry ice" (frozen CO_2) is not consistent with the temperature $-39°$ C. which is far above the dry ice temperature of $-80°$ C. Hoyle once said that maybe there are seas of oil on Venus and the atmosphere is "smog." But he thought then that the earth's oil had been coagulated from hydrocarbon molecules collected on cosmic dust. But the earth's oil can be shown by isotopic analysis of the carbon to have passed through a life cycle. Oil really does come from decayed fish. There are probably no fish on Venus!

To sum up: Our knowledge of Venus consists mostly of ignorance, plus some uncertainty and a good deal of speculation. The only things accurately known are its orbit (almost circular, mean radius 66,800,000 miles) and

Fig. 14. Venus, taken in blue light with the 200-inch Hale Telescope.

its period (224.7008 mean solar [earth] days). Thus, space probes sent out to orbit near Venus will at once bring back much new information, especially if they can sample the outer atmosphere. Soft landings on Venus will present major problems. We do not know whether we will strike land or water or—oil! But the atmosphere may be a great help by permitting parachuting in the final stages of descent. If Venus does not spin on its axis faster than it goes around the sun, a radio transmitter on its surface will be shielded from the earth for several months at a time—and we can only hope it lands on the side that is toward the earth when the planet is nearest to us. Yet, this side might be very cold; on the other hand, the sunny side might be very hot. Or do stupendous winds help equalize the temperature?

When we start penetrating such mysteries we should be prepared for many surprises and many disappointments. And, especially, we should move cautiously to obtain all possible information from the earth and from relatively "cheap" flights before the most complex (and therefore uncertain) ones are undertaken.

Mars

Mars is the favorite planet among earthly humans. Why? Because it is not too far away (34.5 million miles, minimum), its orbit is outside the earth's orbit, and when it is nearest us we are looking at its fully sunlit face. Hence, we can see more of it. Also, its atmosphere is quite transparent and we can see certain surface features.

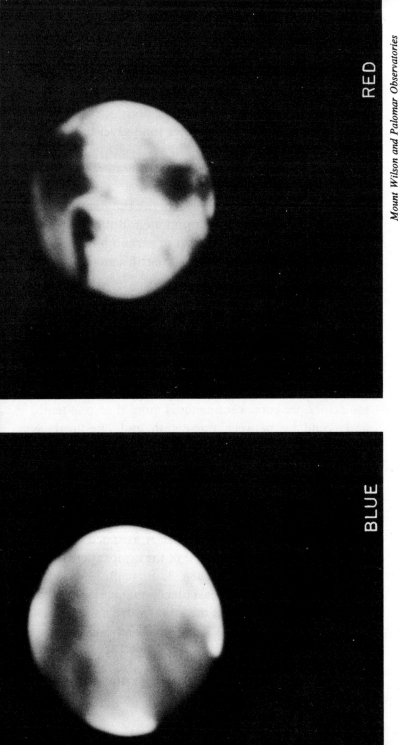

RED

BLUE

Mount Wilson and Palomar Observatories

Fig. 15. *Mars, taken in blue and red light with 200-inch telescope.*

(Fig. 15) Mars is only one-tenth the mass of earth, and a little over one-half the diameter (one-seventh the volume) of the earth. Gravity on its surface is two-fifths of that on the earth. The surface temperatures seem to range from 30° C. (100° F.) down to −60° C. (−96° F.). On the average it's a bit chilly, for the sun delivers only one-half as much energy per unit area. But it is not too impossibly cold for the support of certain kinds of life; it may be much like certain of the earth's arctic regions. Its equatorial regions may be quite pleasant, by our standards.

The atmosphere, however, presents a problem. Atmospheric pressure at the surface is only one-tenth that at the surface of the earth. However, because gravity is less and hence the weight of a given mass of gas (i.e., the weight of a given molecule) is less, the number of molecules per cubic centimeter is more than one-tenth, and could be between one-eighth and one-third, as great as on earth, depending on chemical constitution. However, the only gas definitely identified in the atmosphere is CO_2, yet the measured mass of CO_2 is only one-eightieth the total mass of the atmosphere. Neither water vapor nor oxygen can exist to more than 1 percent or .1 percent respectively. It is then assumed, without definite evidence, that the rest of the atmosphere (or at least 97.5 percent) is nitrogen. Is it, really? We don't know. This is merely the least objectionable assumption.

Though water vapor in the atmosphere has not been detected, the white polar caps, which advance and recede in the Martian change of seasons, seem surely to be frost or snow.

And the great areas on the Martian surface which change color with the seasons could well be a form of plant life—e.g., moss. Plants live on CO_2, and if there is some snow—and hence a little moisture—there is no reason why plants should not grow. Maybe in a few more billion years the plants could convert enough CO_2 into oxygen so that higher forms of life (oxygen-breathing) could develop. But there is not enough CO_2 to give a very rich oxygen atmosphere. Presumably the earth is far ahead of Mars in the life-evolutionary history—possibly because Mars is too cold for plants to grow (and thus make oxygen) at such prodigious rates as in the earth's primeval jungles.

Curiously enough, Mars rotates about its axis at nearly the same rate as does the earth—its day is 24 hours, 37 minutes, 22.58 seconds long—and, since its axis, like the earth's, is inclined 25° to the plane of rotation about the sun, it has its seasons like the earth. However, the Martian year (period of rotation about the sun) is about 687 of our days long (673 Martian days), or nearly two of our years. Thus, if the Martian calendar were divided into twelve months, the months would average about 56 days each.

All in all, Mars seems to be mostly a chilly, sandy desert, with no oceans and no clouds as we know them. Such atmospheric blurs as are seen appear to be dust clouds—or possibly, at certain times, extremely high-altitude clouds of ice crystals. It is not a very attractive looking place to live, especially without much oxygen, and yet, because of the lack of oceans, it has nearly as much land area as the earth. No mountains can be seen, hence, the surface must be quite flat.

But there is much that we do not know. What is the atmosphere? Is there really plant life? If so, what is its chemical constitution? Is it based on organic molecules similar to those we know? Or some quite different kinds of compounds? Does the photosynthetic process exist? (We do not detect the characteristic colors of chlorophyll.) Is oxygen produced and CO_2 consumed?

And what of the surface? Is it dust, sand, rock, or what? Why are there no mountains? Is Mars too small to have internal strains, earth faults, or volcanic disturbances? A look at the surface and subsurface materials would be enormously revealing, and a seismograph station would tell us still more.

The soft landing of an instrumented package on Mars is possible, but difficult. A reasonable trajectory from earth to Mars would require, in the most favorable case, a travel time of 140 to 160 days. When the probe arrives, Mars will already be nearly 90 million miles from the earth. Not an easy target to hit! If we land a radio on Mars, its distance from us will continually increase for over a year to the maximum of about 210 million miles; it will then decrease until it reaches its minimum of 35 million miles after over two years. Thus, radio communication will have to be assured over long times as well as long distances.

The Mars landing will be greatly aided (as compared to the moon, and like Venus) by its atmosphere (we can use a parachute!)—provided we are successful in not striking the atmosphere at too great a speed; i.e., provided our retro-rockets fire at just the right moment and with the probe pointed in the right direction. Fortunately, our solar batteries will keep on working (during the Martian days), as they will presumably not work under the opaque clouds of Venus. However, serious obstacles still intervene in getting probes even within a million miles or so of such a distant fast-moving object.

Other planets

Every other solar planet offers its interesting aspects and its many mysteries. Tiny Mercury is too close to the sun for comfort of a space expedition, and too close also for good visual observations from the earth. Giant Jupiter—more massive than all the other planets put together—is almost big enough to be a second sun. It is 11 times the diameter of the earth and 318 times the mass. Gravity on its visible surface is 2.6 times that on the earth—so a 200-pound man would weigh 520 pounds! However, Jupiter is apparently composed mostly of hydrogen and helium (as is the sun). If there is no radioactive heating, the planet may be very cold and, at the great interior pressures, hydrogen and helium would be

Mount Wilson and Palomar Observat

Fig. 16. *Jupiter, showing large red spot; also the satellite Ganymede (upper right) and its shadow (upper left center). Taken in blue light with 200-inch telescope.*

solid. High-altitude clouds completely obscure any view of any "surface," however. (Fig. 16.) The great distance to Jupiter (400,000,000 miles minimum) means great difficulty in even a "near-miss" probe. A new artificial Jupiter satellite (to add to the twelve visible moons it already has) would be a most valuable achievement—but is clearly a long way in the future.

New mystery was added to the Jupiter story by the discovery that Jupiter is a source of radio radiation. Do these originate in giant Jovian thunderstorms? Or in some other atmospheric or surface effect? Or what?

Majestic Saturn (Fig. 17), too, will bear a closer look —but it is very far away.

The sun

The most important object in our solar system is the sun itself. Clearly, we are not going to send probes into or even very near the sun. However, probes which go into orbits, like the earth's orbit, around the sun have already been achieved. If properly equipped, such probes, even though at distances of 60 to 100 million miles from the sun, can yield valuable information. Infrared and ultraviolet pictures of the sun would be enormously useful. Measurements of radio, x-ray, and gamma-ray emissions which cannot reach the earth would also be of interest.

In the minds of many, however, the most interesting thing about interplanetary space is that, possibly as far out as Pluto or beyond, we are still in the sun's atmos-

Mount Wilson and Palomar Observatories

Fig. 17. Saturn, taken in blue light with 200-inch telescope.

Fig. 18. Sun emitting large active flare, 140,000 miles high, July 17, 1917. Photographed in light of calcium. White dot

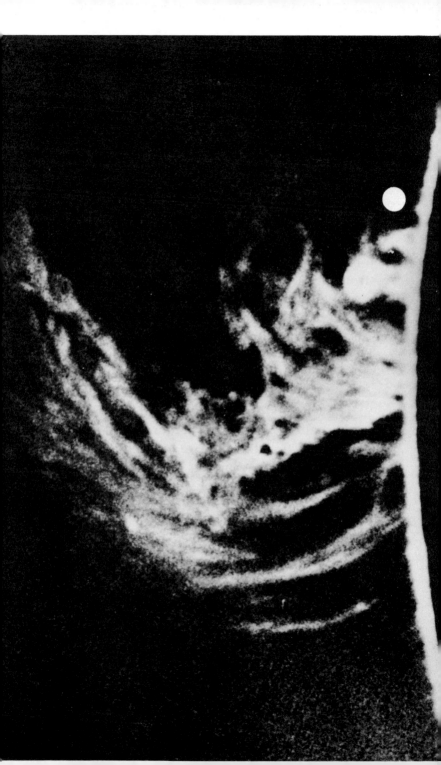

phere. That is, clouds of ionized or un-ionized atoms, probably mostly hydrogen but containing other elements too, are being emitted from the sun all the time. Sometimes the clouds are blown off in great explosions or flares (Fig. 18); some gas is being ejected continuously. These streams of particles contribute to cosmic rays, to auroras, to magnetic storms, and maybe to other earthly phenomena, including the weather. But, we can observe these clouds directly only by getting well away from the earth's magnetic field. It is estimated that the density of matter in the solar system, away from any planet, is about 1,000 atoms per cubic centimeter— about 10^{-16} atmosphere, or a billion times better than any vacuum obtainable on earth. But, still, enough atoms could be collected by a satellite to be analyzed, and an interesting story would surely be revealed.

The solar system, then, is something to occupy our space ventures for decades or centuries to come. Yet, as we get away from the earth, we shall surely want to take a look with our instruments into the vast reaches of space beyond our tiny solar system.

IV
The Universe

THE POSSIBILITY of astronomical equipment being placed in a satellite orbiting far above the earth's atmosphere, and conceivably someday having an observatory on the moon, has resulted in an intensively renewed interest in astronomy and astrophysics. Many observations which can never be made from the earth's surface may soon be feasible, and a host of new data can be expected to solve many mysteries and answer many questions about the size, structure, origin, and evolutionary history of the universe. These new observations will not all come quickly, of course, but the next fifty years should see enormous advances in our understanding of cosmology and cosmogony.

There have, in fact, been enormous advances in the past fifty years. It is astonishing to remember that it was only one hundred years ago that the first measurements were made of the distances to even the nearest stars (by observing the parallax, or apparent change in position, of a star as the earth moves in its great orbit about the sun). But not until the completion of the 60-inch telescope on Mt. Wilson in 1909, and the 100-inch telescope in 1916, was it possible to begin to appreciate the vast distances to the other stars and to see that the hitherto mysterious "nebulae" (hazy spots) in the sky were themselves giant collections of stars at even more stupendous distances.

Kepler had assumed that all the stars were about .1 of a light-year away from the sun. (A light-year is the distance that light travels in a year, at 186,000 miles per second. A time unit is used as a measure of distance for the same reason of convenience that we say Los Angeles is 5 hours from New York—by jet airplane rather than by a light beam!) In 1920 it was found that the central stars in our Milky Way were 26,000 light-years away. And only since 1925 has it been gradually established that the other galaxies of stars, the nebulae, are all millions, and some even billions, of light-years away. Figure 19 shows the 200-inch Hale telescope at Palomar Mountain, and Figures 20 through 24 show some views of the universe taken with it and with other telescopes.

At this point it is useful to recount the methods by which these great distances are measured—or rather estimated. Obviously, parallax measurements fail completely for all but the very nearest stars. Only quite near ones (less than 30 light-years) have a parallax as much as .1 second of arc. For distant stars the only method available is the method of brightness; the farther away an object is, the fainter it appears. But how do we know whether a given faint object is really small but close, or bright and far away? It was Shapley and Leavitt who

Fig. 19. The 200-inch Hale Telescope of the Palomar Observatory pointing to zenith, seen from the east.

found that there was a certain class of variable or pulsating stars (called the Cepheid variables) for which there was a very definite relation between the period of pulsation and the absolute brightness. Hence, if two Cepheids were observed with the same period, but one appeared 4 times fainter than the other, then the fainter one must be twice as far away. (Apparent brightness falls as the square of the distance.) By measuring the periods and apparent brightness, a distance scale could be established. In this way the distances to stars in our own Milky Way galaxy—out to 50,000 light-years—were established.

Later it was found that the nearby nebulae could, with the 100-inch and later with the 200-inch telescope, be resolved into stars, and some Cepheid variables were identified in them. Hence, the distances to these nebulae were estimated. However, in more distant nebulae individual stars cannot be resolved at all. Fortunately, certain clusters of stars have been found—consisting of many thousands of stars—whose absolute brightness seems to be fixed and can thus be used as distance indicators. Finally, it is found that certain types of nebulae themselves (consisting of 100 billion stars) are of similar average brightness, hence, their apparent brightness is itself an indication of distance.

However, here one enters into the realm of great uncertainties, and just within the past few years new observations have doubled and then quadrupled the estimated distance scale for the distant galaxies. Objects thought to be .5 billion light-years away are now clearly seen to be 2 billion or more light-years distant. This is a vastly important fact—as we shall soon see.

However, even if we do not know distance accurately, we do know that all the stars of the universe are collected into groups called galaxies, each galaxy containing up to 100 billion or so stars. There are certainly hundreds of millions of galaxies in the universe—and these in turn are clumped into clusters. On the average, however, the galaxies appear to be nearly uniformly distributed in space. Though there are local clusters, the total density of galaxies—say in a spherical shell 1 million light-years thick and 100 million light-years away—is the same as the density in a shell 500 million or 1,000 million light-years away. If the density is the same, however, this means that the total number in the shell 1,000 million light-years distant is 100 times as great as in a shell only 100 million light-years in radius, since the volume of a shell of given thickness increases as the square of the radius.

This fact gives rise to one of the famous paradoxes in astronomy known as Olber's paradox—first set forth in 1826. Since the light received from a given star falls as the inverse square of the distance and since the number of stars increases as the square of the distance, the total light from all stars at 10 light-years should be the same as for all at 100 or 1,000 or 10,000 light-years. Hence, if the universe were infinite in extent, and uniformly populated, the intensity of radiation at any point would be infinite. Since the night sky is not brilliantly illuminated but is in fact quite dark, clearly the universe either is not uniformly populated or else it is not infinitely large, or the inverse square law does not hold.

In the early days astronomers asserted that the second view was correct and that the universe indeed did not extend beyond the boundaries of our own Milky Way. Later, when it was clear that the faint nebulae seen on photographs with the large telescopes were in themselves galaxies like the Milky Way, but very distant and apparently uniformly distributed, Olber's paradox again came into prominence. Clearly, a uniform distribution of stars now seems to be the most tenable assumption. Why, then, is the whole night sky not as bright as the sun, and why are we not all burned to a crisp?

There are various ways out of the dilemma, and we actually do not yet know what is the true answer.

But one staggering new fact was unearthed by Hubble and Humason in 1925—namely, the distant galaxies are receding from us. The universe is expanding! This idea has become so well known in recent years that we are inclined to forget what an extraordinary concept it is. For thousands of years, everyone believed that all the stars were at the same distance from the earth—attached to the inside of a hollow sphere. Even when it was found they were at varying distances, and grouped in huge galaxies and clusters of galaxies, it was still assumed that the universe was static. But now we know that the distant galaxies are all receding from us and

Fig. 20. *A portion of the Milky Way.*

from each other, and that the velocity of recession is greater for the most distant galaxies—increasing just in proportion to their distance. The ratio of the distance to the velocity is called Hubble's constant. This provides two ways out of Olber's paradox:

1. If the universe is expanding, the expansion must have begun at some time in the past—a time which can be determined by measuring the velocities and the distances. Since this is a finite time in the past, the universe has not had time to attain an infinite extent as yet—and a boundary will someday be found, certainly at a distance where the recession velocity equals the velocity of light. No stars could have got farther away than that since the creation. Hence we have a finite universe and no paradox.

2. When a star is moving rapidly away from an observer, the light waves it emits are stretched out. That is how the velocity of recession is determined. This is the well-known Doppler effect. But this means that the energy reaching the observer is also less each second since fewer light waves arrive. Hence, an object which is receding rapidly will also appear fainter. And as the velocity of recession approaches the velocity of light, the stretching out becomes greater and the apparent brightness will approach zero. Hence the most distant galaxies do not supply as much light as the nearby ones—the inverse square law does not hold and the paradox is solved. In other words, as Fred Hoyle puts it, our night sky is dark because the universe is expanding. Even though

Fig. 21. NGC 224 Great Nebula in Andromeda. Messier 31. Satellite nebulae NGC 205 and 221 also shown. Taken with 48-inch schmidt telescope.

Mount Wilson and Palomar Observatories

the universe were infinite, the light of the night sky would be finite.

Modern measurements of the distances of the most distant objects for which velocity measurements can be made give values of 1.2 billion light-years—at which point the recession velocity is one-fifth the velocity of light. Clearly, it took such objects 6 billion years to get that far out—and adding the 1.2 billion years for the light to get back, we conclude that the expansion must have begun about 7.2 billion years ago. Maybe it was 10, or even 15. The distance measurements are that uncertain.

But if some catastrophic expansion event was initiated some 10 billion years ago, what kind of an event was it and what has been the history of the universe since?

It was George Gamow who first explored the idea that the universe began as a gigantic cloud of neutrons, packed so closely together as to constitute a giant object almost as dense as an atomic nucleus. This supernucleus then blew up and, as it expanded, the neutrons decayed to protons and electrons; the protons coagulated into helium nuclei, helium to oxygen; and then, by successive capture of neutrons, all elements in the periodic table were formed. All this must have taken place, Gamow figured, in the first few *minutes* after "creation."

Although it had some astonishing successes, the Gamow theory had to modified because it could not account for the formation of all the nuclei. Now, following the work of Fowler and others, it is believed that most of the creation of the elements takes place all the time in the interiors of stars. We now assume that the initial universe was a ball of hydrogen and that this expanded for a long time until the temperature was lowered to the point where gravitational forces could be effective. Under gravity, clumping into great clouds took place, followed by local clumping into protogalaxies—and, finally, fine-grained clumping into stars.

As a single star begins to form under gravitational attraction, the temperature rises as gravitational energy is converted into heat. Within such a star of hydrogen the pressure and temperature at the center will rise until hydrogen coalesces into helium. Then, suddenly, a new source of energy comes into existence which may prevent further collapse and produce a stable star. Inside the star helium is being formed—and, eventually, all the elements in the periodic table can be formed by successive capture of protons, neutrons, and alpha particles (helium nuclei).

The precise reactions by which helium and the heavier elements are formed have been worked out in surprisingly satisfactory detail by W. A. Fowler, Salpeter, and the Burbidges. They have traced the reactions almost element by element up to uranium and can explain why some elements are rare, others more abundant. We cannot take time here even to summarize the results of their analysis. We will examine only the first steps.

It is simple to see that in a hot gas of protons there will

be frequent collisions in which two protons will join to form a deuteron with the ejection of a positron. Indeed this reaction begins to take place with high probability at a temperature of about 5 million degrees Centigrade. We can represent this process by the equation,

$$H^1 + H^1 \rightarrow D^2 + \beta^+.$$

As an appreciable density of D^2 is built up, we then get the following reaction:

$$D^2 + D^2 \rightarrow He^3 + n \text{ (n stands for a neutron)}.$$

It now appears that the next reaction is

$$He^3 + He^3 \rightarrow He^4 + 2H^1.$$

The net result is as though we had converted four protons into helium:

$$4H^1 \rightarrow He^4 + 2\beta^+$$

and the total energy released is 26.7 million electron-volts for each He^4 nucleus formed. This is an enormous quantity of energy—plenty to account for all the heat of a sun or star, and still allow the star to "burn" for billions of years.

Ninety-three percent of the atoms in the universe are *still* hydrogen, and most of the remaining 7 percent are helium. Thus, in all the ages since the first stars were formed only 7 percent of the original hydrogen has been consumed.

But, sooner or later, the hydrogen at the core of a star where the above reactions take place will get used up. Then what? First, of course, since the energy source is then gone, the star will begin to contract under gravity. This will compress the core and heat it up. Its tempera-

Fig. 22. NGC 3031 spiral nebula in Ursa Major. Messier 81. Taken with 200-inch telescope.

Mount Wilson and Palomar Observatories

ture may well rise to 100 million degrees Centigrade. At this temperature the following reaction can occur:

$$He^4 + He^4 \rightarrow Be^8.$$

However, Be^8 is highly unstable and immediately breaks up again into two helium nuclei. This would appear to be the end of the process. It turns out, however, that Be^8 does last for a short time and hence a very small concentration of it will be built up. Then we could have

$$Be^8 + He^4 \rightarrow C^{12}$$

and a new stable element is formed and more energy released. Laboratory measurements have shown, indirectly, that the capture of He by Be^8 is a resonant reaction and has a very high probability at these temperatures. Hence C^{12} will be formed in quantity—and the star has a new energy supply. From now on, successive captures of He^4 build up O^{16}, Ne^{20}, Mg^{24}. Then even more complex reactions may take place, resulting in neutron emission. Capture of the neutrons can then in succession build up most of the heavier elements.

Not all stars, of course, go through the cycles smoothly or at the same speed. Heavy stars will burn their fuel more rapidly; lighter ones, more slowly. Sometimes, at certain stages, instabilities may set in and tremendous explosions may result. Novae or supernovae are then seen by earthly observers.

These gigantic explosions, spewing vast quantities of gas and dust into interstellar space, may start new cycles of star making. For these gas-dust clouds, which are seen throughout all the galaxies, may condense into stars.

Fig. 23. NGC 4565 spiral nebula in Coma Berenices, seen edge on. Note dark band of dust. Photographed on an unfiltered red sensitive plate. Taken with 200-inch telescope.

Mount Wilson and Palomar Observatories

And in these stars—since He, C, O and the heavier elements, especially iron, already exist—new nuclear reactions may take place. It is in such "second-generation" stars that the famous carbon cycle can occur, in which C^{12} serves as a catalyst to convert H into He with the corresponding energy release. Our sun is one of these second-generation stars, condensed only 4.5 billion years ago out of a cloud of dust.

Only 4.5 billion years ago!

Yes, the age of the solar system may be considered as now quite well established from careful uranium-lead ratio measurements on rocks and meteorites. It is then evident why such great importance is attached to the Hubble constant—the ratio of the distance of a nebula to its velocity of recession. For this ratio—the same for all observed nebulae—sets the time scale for the universe. It was not many years ago that the value of this constant appeared to be only 3 billion years—less than the age of the solar system—a most embarrassing situation. Improved distance measurements have all tended to increase the Hubble constant—by increasing the estimates of distances. Now if it is 7 billion years or, as some say, 10 to 15 billion years, the time scale of the universe has become very long and there was plenty of time for galaxies to coagulate, for stars to form and blow up, and then for stars like our sun to condense out of the gaseous debris.

All of this makes a very attractive picture: A universe brought into being by a localized cataclysmic event some

Fig. 24. A cluster of nebulae in Corona Borealis. The distance is about 120 million light-years. Each small elongated hazy object is a galaxy of possibly 100 billion stars. Taken with 200-inch telescope. Mount Wilson and Palomar Observatories

10 billion years ago. The event resulted in vast clouds of hydrogen being hurtled out into space at speeds apparently up nearly to the speed of light. And all through the ages these clouds have kept receding from each other with these same velocities—with local condensations occurring due to gravitational forces, but the vast expansion itself having slowed down only slightly, if at all, by gravitational forces.

It is only fair to point out, however, that some astronomers of great note do not accept this theory at all. These scientists argue that if the universe is over 10 billion years old, why not try assuming that it is infinitely old—i.e., that an observer 5 or 10 or 50 billion years ago (not on our earth, of course) would have seen the same kind of universe as we see now—billions of galaxies, distributed the same way in space, all receding from each other. Individual stars, individual galaxies, come and go like clouds racing across the sky. But as the clouds can come and go while the *condition* of cloudiness remains, so galaxies come and go while the universe remains in what is called "a steady state."

Whether one prefers a universe with a beginning (and presumably also with an end) or a universe without beginning or end may be a matter of taste. The question is, which idea correlates and predicts the largest number of facts? So far both pictures are in agreement with the facts as we know them. It is then only a matter of taste.

A sudden beginning is, to some, a puzzling, even a revolting, idea. As Fred Hoyle says: "How can we believe the laws of physics suddenly came into being at a certain date? Why not assume they have always acted unless the facts clearly deny it?" On the other hand, he must admit that if a cataclysmic origin involves a nonphysical event, the steady-state theory involves also a phenomenon not yet observed—probably even unobservable. This is the continuous creation of matter. If the universe has always looked as it now looks, clearly new matter must be created to fill the vast voids created as the matter visible 100 billion years ago expands outward and eventually tumbles over the horizon of visibility. The amount of matter which needs to appear in the universe each second to maintain the same average density is not large—one hydrogen atom each second for each 4 million cubic kilometers of space. This means, according to Hoyle, one atom each century for each volume the size of the Empire State Building; 250,000 atoms per second for a volume the size of the earth. Within the entire universe to the outermost galaxies this amounts to 10^{32} tons per second. This, of course, is just the rate at which galaxies "disappear from view" as they recede—and accelerate—eventually getting up to the velocity of light, and therefore becoming invisible.

Unfortunately, the arguments for and against the two theories are exceedingly complex. Both assume the same processes for atom-building within the stars; both assume the same sort of life cycle for each individual star and for each galaxy. The crucial point seems to be: are the galaxies receding with the same velocities they acquired at the "beginning of time"—each galaxy retaining the same velocity for all time, except for a possible slight slowing up due to the gravitational pull of all other galaxies? Or is each galaxy accelerating—speeding up as it recedes—being pushed outward, as it were, by the pressure of new matter being created behind it?

We cannot answer this question directly, of course. We cannot imagine how the acceleration is attained— i.e., what is the repulsive force which causes it? But we cannot imagine, either, what the initial cataclysm was like and what caused it.

Some of the puzzles may be resolved if we can get more powerful telescopes which can see farther into space. Does the density of matter remain constant out to 2, 3, 6 billion light-years? Do the velocities still increase linearly with distance? If so, then at some 6 billion light-years they reach the velocity of light. Do galaxies go faster than that? If so, we could never see them. Does the Hubble law break down as one gets to one-half or three-fourths or nine-tenths the velocity of light? So far, we can see out only to galaxies receding with possibly one-fifth the velocity of light. New telescope "seeing" techniques—possibly electronic in nature—will be needed to see, and to take spectrographs any farther. Or else we must lift our telescopes and spectroscopes above the atmosphere to get still better seeing. It is exasperating to find, just as we get to the interesting range of velocities, our observing methods failing us. But space laboratories may someday bring the extension to our vision required to answer some of these most absorbing questions in science.

Our ignorance so vastly exceeds our knowledge that it is the unknown things, not the known ones, that are the most numerous and the most interesting. Because of the enormous difficulty and cost of many space enterprises, they will not come as rapidly as we might like. And, yet, many of the scientific projects that may be undertaken will yield enough knowledge to be worth the cost and trouble. For no venture is more ultimately profitable than adding just a little bit to man's knowledge of the universe in which he lives.

Appendix

Much has happened in the field of space exploration since the original manuscript of this book was prepared in 1959. Many space capsules have been launched for the purpose of taking scientific measurements, and both the Russians and the Americans have succeeded in orbiting man-carrying capsules around the earth and bringing them back safely. The United States has vastly increased its space program and is developing new rocket boosters, new types of space capsule for carrying scientific instruments, culminating in a projected attempt to land human beings on the moon by the year 1970.

Though many new events have occurred, all of the basic scientific data contained in this book, and the outline of the problems to be investigated, remain much the same as they were three years ago. The following notes, however, may be useful in providing more recent information relevant to certain passages in the book. The notes are listed by the page numbers in the main text where the subject is discussed.

Note to page 10

The following is a list of the principal space capsules successfully launched since October 1, 1959:

This is a special supplement for the paperback edition *Introduction to Space* by Lee A. DuBridge, California Institute of Technology, Pasadena.

Table II. SUMMARY OF SPACE VEHICLES SUCCESSFULLY
LAUNCHED SINCE OCTOBER 1, 1959*
(TO FEBRUARY 27, 1962)

Name	Date	Status or Lifetime
Lunik 3	October 4, 1959	Lunar probe (199 days)
Explorer 7	October 13, 1959	In orbit
Discoverer 7	November 7, 1959	19 days
Discoverer 8	November 20, 1959	110 days
Pioneer 5	March 11, 1960	Solar orbit
Tiros 1	April 1, 1960	In orbit
Transit 1B	April 13, 1960	In orbit
Discoverer 11	April 15, 1960	11 days
Sputnik 4	May 15, 1960	In orbit
Midas 2	May 24, 1960	In orbit
Transit 2A	June 22, 1960	In orbit
Discoverer 13	August 10, 1960	96 days (capsule recovered from ocean)
Echo 1	August 12, 1960	In orbit
Discoverer 14	August 18, 1960	29 days (capsule recovered in air)
Sputnik 5	August 19, 1960	1 day
Discoverer 15	September 13, 1960	35 days
Courier 1B	October 4, 1960	In orbit
Explorer 8	November 3, 1960	In orbit
Discoverer 17	November 12, 1960	48 days (capsule recovered in air)
Tiros 2	November 23, 1960	In orbit
Sputnik 6	December 1, 1960	1 day
Discoverer 18	December 7, 1960	115 days (capsule recovered in air)
Discoverer 19	December 20, 1960	34 days
Samos 2	January 31, 1961	In orbit
Sputnik 7	February 4, 1961	22 days
Sputnik 8	February 12, 1961	Solar orbit
Explorer 9	February 16, 1961	In orbit

* From *Space Log* published by Space Technology Laboratories

Name	Date	Status or Lifetime
Discoverer 20	February 17, 1961	In orbit
Discoverer 21	February 18, 1961	In orbit
Transit 3B/Lofti	February 21, 1961	37 days
Sputnik 9	March 9, 1961	Spacecraft recovered on land
Sputnik 10	March 25, 1961	Spacecraft recovered on land
Explorer 10	March 25, 1961	?
Discoverer 23	April 8, 1961	In orbit
Vostok 1	April 12, 1961	Manned spacecraft recovered on land
Explorer 11	April 27, 1961	In orbit
Discoverer 25	June 16, 1961	26 days (capsule recovered from ocean)
Transit 4A	June 29, 1961	In orbit
Discoverer 26	July 7, 1961	151 days (capsule recovered in air)
Tiros 3	July 12, 1961	In orbit
Midas 3	July 12, 1961	In orbit
Vostok 2	August 6, 1961	Manned spacecraft recovered on land
Explorer 12	August 15, 1961	In orbit
Ranger 1	August 23, 1961	7 days
Explorer 13	August 25, 1961	3 days
Discoverer 29	August 30, 1961	11 days
Discoverer 30	September 12, 1961	90 days (capsule recovered in air)
Mercury-Atlas 4	September 13, 1961	Spacecraft recovered from ocean
Discoverer 31	September 17, 1961	39 days
Discoverer 32	October 13, 1961	31 days (capsule recovered in air)
Midas 4	October 21, 1961	In orbit
Discoverer 34	November 5, 1961	In orbit
Discoverer 35	November 15, 1961	18 days (capsule recovered in air)
Transit 4B	November 15, 1961	In orbit
Ranger 2	November 18, 1961	2 days
Mercury-Atlas 5	November 29, 1961	Spacecraft recovered from ocean

Name	*Date*	*Status or Lifetime*
Discoverer 36	December 12, 1961	In orbit
Ranger 3	January 26, 1962	Lunar probe; in solar orbit
Tiros 4	February 8, 1962	In orbit
Mercury-Atlas 6	February 20, 1962	Manned spacecraft recovered from ocean
Discoverer 38	February 27, 1962	In orbit (capsule recovered in air)

In summary, the United States has successfully launched 68 space capsules, of which 61 went into orbits encircling the earth, 4 went into solar orbits, and 28 are still in earth orbits. The Russians have launched 14 capsules, of which 1 is still in solar orbit.

Note to page 34

The recovery of a space capsule from orbit had not been achieved in 1959. Since that time 10 Discoverer capsules have been safely recovered, as well as the Mercury capsule in which Colonel John H. Glenn was a passenger and pilot.

Note to page 35

The maximum distance at which radio signals from a space capsule have been received is now 22,462,000 miles in the case of Pioneer 5. Methods for keeping a high-gain antenna pointed at the earth have been worked out, and large and sensitive antenna-receivers have been built at various places on the earth to aid in extending communication to still greater distances.

Note to page 69

Measurements during 1961–62 carried on at the Caltech

radio observatory at Bishop, California, have shown that the radio radiations from Jupiter are due to a band of charged particles trapped in Jupiter's magnetic field, very similar to the Van Allen layers around the earth. This layer has been named the Bolton layer, in honor of John G. Bolton, formerly director of the Bishop observatory, who made the discovery. The intensity of the radio radiations suggests a relatively dense cloud of charged particles apparently trapped in an extremely strong magnetic field associated with this planet.

Note to page 82

Observations at the Bishop Radio Observatory and at the Palomar Observatory resulted in the discovery of a galaxy whose distance is estimated at 6 billion light years and which is receding at a velocity nearly one-half the velocity of light. These measurements give a new "age of the universe" figure in the vicinity of 18 billion years.